Forever in Our Hearts

Written by Kristina Andrade
Illustrated by Tanja Varcelija

Dear Mrs Solvason,
Thank you for
doing writers workshop
with Evelyn. I love that
You instilled a love of
creativity and writing.
I cannot wait to see where it takes
her.
Kristina
Andrade

#ForeverinOurHeartsBook
www.foreverinourheartsbook.com

Dedication

This book is for all the children who have felt the love of a
new baby and had to say goodbye too soon.
You are strong and you are loved!
Your angel baby is in heaven with God,
always watching over you and your family.

Acknowledgments

A very heartfelt and special thank you to those
who helped bring this book to life, nearly all of whom have
tragically experienced a miscarriage personally...

We sincerely hope this story will help families, especially
those with young children, heal and process the big feelings
along the way, just as writing and sharing it has helped us.

Thank you!

Our family is very special, just like your family.

We laugh together. We go to the park together. We eat together. We are blessed!

Recently, we got some very exciting news. Our family is growing! We are expecting a new baby.

We talk about how Mommy's tummy will grow bigger and bigger. Mommy says, "When my tummy looks as big as a watermelon, that's when the baby will come out."

We tell the new baby, "We love you so much!" We talk about where the new baby will sleep. I'll let the new baby have my crib, since I am going to be a big brother.

Our family and friends cheer and hug us tight when we tell them about the new baby. They even ask us if we want it to be a boy or a girl. My sister always says, "We don't know. It's a surprise and God gets to pick." I think it's going to be a boy, though.

Thinking about our future with a new baby is very exciting!

One evening, Mommy has a tummy ache. Mommy is calm but serious.
She tells us that she needs our help at bedtime. I ask Mommy,
"Do you need some Band-Aids?" I think that might help.

Mommy snuggles us tight as
we read our bedtime stories.
She tucks us in, sings two
songs, says good night, and
tells us she loves us so much!

When we wake up in the morning our nana comes to our rooms to get us. Nana says, "Mommy and Daddy went to the hospital for Mommy's tummy ache, and they will be home soon." We enjoy playing at home with Nana. We don't know that things are going to change very quickly.

Mommy and Daddy send us a picture message with a BIG rainbow in the sky above them. It feels so good to see their faces and the beautiful colors of the magical rainbow beaming across the sky.

When Mommy and Daddy come home,
they give us big hugs. They say they love us
and that they have something to tell us.

They say that our new baby died. Mommy says, "Our new baby was growing, but then the baby stopped growing. Something was wrong."

Daddy says, "The baby wasn't healthy and it needed to come out. So Mommy got a tummy ache and started cramping and that helped the tiny little baby to come out. The doctor helped Mommy to stay healthy and strong for our family."

My sister and I hug our parents. For the first time, we are all very sad, a little mad, and really confused. These are feelings that our family feels together. This is something we have never talked about or felt before.

We are reminded by our parents that it's okay to feel all of these BIG feelings. God's plan for the new baby wasn't what we had in mind. But God needed the new baby by his side to watch over us.
It's hard for us to understand, so we talk about it a lot. We say that our new baby grew its angel wings that day and went to heaven.

There are times when we have BIG feelings
that are almost impossible to control!
We get sad and mad. My sister often asks,
"Why? Why did the new baby die?"

I tell Mommy and Daddy, "I'm not going to get to give the new baby a high five or hugs!" I even yell, "I'm not going to be a big brother anymore! And that makes me so, so, so sad!"

Our family was truly changed by the new baby's presence, even though Mommy was pregnant for just a little while. This very unexpected life event is called a miscarriage. It's a new word for us to learn and sometimes this word causes people to feel BIG feelings.

My mommy tells me, "You'll always be a big brother, even though the baby is in heaven." I feel the new baby in my heart!

Especially at night time as I lay in my crib, I ask my parents if we can talk or pray about the new baby. They always say, "Yes!" I feel so full of love, even though the new baby left our lives so soon.

We love you, new baby, and know you are smiling in heaven as you watch over our family! We miss you, but we know you are at peace with God by your side. Even though we will never hold you in our arms, we will hold you forever in our hearts.

About the Author

Kristina holds her bachelor's degree in Child Development, specializing in Early Childhood Education, with more than a decade of experience working professionally with toddlers and preschoolers.

She's also a mom of two and has a rainbow baby on the way. After experiencing her own miscarriage in 2020, Kristina felt like God was calling her to share her family's story from her son's perspective.

Forever in Our Hearts, inspired by those real life events, is her first book, and she sincerely hopes that reading it may help families experiencing miscarriage heal, the same way writing it helped her.

About the Illustrator

Tanja has been illustrating children's stories for seven years.

Her passion for drawing started when she was a little girl.
She studied and began working as a graphic designer and
eventually discovered illustration as her true passion.

Her love for children's books comes from her grandmother,
who would tell her stories that they'd draw together.

Tanja experienced a miscarriage between her own two
children, and felt this story was very important to share.

Made in the USA
Monee, IL
23 September 2021